Jon Scieszka's TRUCKTOWN
on Reading Street

THE YELLOW BOX

PEARSON

Glenview, Illinois • Boston, Massachusetts • Chandler, Arizona
Shoreview, Minnesota • Upper Saddle River, New Jersey

Jack had a blue box.

He had a green box.

He had a yellow box.

2

The blue box is for Max.

Jack got the box to Max.

Max is glad.

3

The green box is for Gabriella.

Jack got the box to Gabriella.

She is glad.

4

The yellow box is for Rosie.

Jack got the box to Rosie.

Is she glad?

5

Jack, my box is red.

Did you mix yellow and red?

This box is for Dan.

6

Sad Jack, I can fix it.

I can hit the box!

BAM!

Rosie did fix it!

Dan got his box.

Jack was glad!